Chipping Campden
Gloucestershire
GL55 6LD UK
Tel: +44 (0) 1386 842000
Fax: +44 (0) 1386 842100
www.campden.co.uk

Guideline No. 33

HACCP in Agriculture: Livestock Production

Supplement 1: Cattle Rearing for Beef Case Study

L. Bedford and C. Knight

2001

Campden & Chorleywood Food Research Association Group comprises
Campden & Chorleywood Food Research Association
and its subsidiary companies
CCFRA Technology Ltd   CCFRA Group Services Ltd   Campden & Chorleywood Magyarország

© CCFRA 2001
ISBN: 0 905942 40 X

FOREWORD

Of all the foods on offer in today's marketplace, meat has received closer attention and more adverse publicity than any other and beef has been singled out for particular attention. As a result, much has been said and written on the subject of the safety of beef.

Because of the way in which HACCP offers a structured approach to considering the hazards and risks associated with the production of food, it is readily applicable to any stage of the food chain. It is therefore heartening to see the use of HACCP in areas where legislation does not yet require it as it is recognition of the value and power of the technique.

It is equally important to note that the HACCP study can only address hazards which are known to exist or can be scientifically proven or predicted. For this reason, the study must be regularly reviewed and updated in the light of new or changed information.

Having carried out a full HACCP study on our beef slaughtering and further processing operation we applaud this publication which will enable our suppliers to present their animals for slaughter in such a way that food safety is not compromised during the cattle rearing process.

David J. Nicholson
Managing Director, Oriel Jones & Son Ltd.

- ii -

PREFACE

HACCP is already established as a system for monitoring food safety in meat production at the abattoir and in food processing. It also provides an appropriate approach to a structured system of controls in livestock primary production. CCFRA Guideline No. 33, *HACCP in Agriculture: Livestock Production* shows how the general principles of HACCP can be applied to agricultural primary production.

This supplement, which has been produced with co-operation from primary producers and food businesses in the meat industry, provides specific guidance on establishing a HACCP system for the rearing of animals for meat production, taking beef cattle as an example. It is designed to be used in conjunction with Guideline 33. The practical guidance in this document is consistent with the HACCP approach defined in CCFRA Technical Manual 38 (*HACCP: A Practical Guide - Second Edition*) which is widely used by food processors and manufacturers. Other case studies in the series cover other livestock enterprises.

Lynn Bedford and Chris Knight
CCFRA

CONTENTS

INTRODUCTION

The aim of this manual is to provide specific guidance on establishing a HACCP system for beef production. The first section gives a brief description of the stages that need to be considered in sequence to develop a HACCP system in animal production. The second section gives a *worked example* to demonstrate a HACCP system in beef production.

The worked example *illustrates* a detailed approach that may be applied to an individual beef rearing operation. This approach requires relevant expertise in terms of animal rearing for beef and of HACCP systems, and the necessary resources to establish and implement a detailed HACCP study. It may be most readily adopted by larger enterprises but is applicable to all sizes of business. The more detailed the approach, the more benefit can be derived by a business in terms of identifying and controlling food safety hazards and product quality aspects. A less detailed approach is possible, and is likely to be appropriate to those organisations with limited resources and/or knowledge of HACCP systems, and in particular smaller animal rearing enterprises. This should, however, be viewed as an initial approach to HACCP - that is, a building block from which a more thorough HACCP system can be developed as more experience is gained.

An effective HACCP system in animal rearing will take time and resources to develop. However, the benefits that can be derived from an effective system include meeting customer requirements, demonstrating conformance with legal requirements and continuous improvement of the management of animal rearing for meat. A HACCP approach is an effective (and cost-effective), logical and structured means of providing a beef production control system. The level of detail of the HACCP system will depend on the nature and size of the business. A larger business might reasonably be expected to have a more thorough system than a smaller operation.

SECTION 1: How to set up and conduct a beef HACCP study

The HACCP system is based on seven principles, and when conducting a HACCP study in agriculture, the seven principles of HACCP may be applied as twelve stages as shown in Figure 1. These include both essential preparation tasks ('Planning' stages 1 to 4), and the principles of HACCP ('Application' stages 5 to 12).

Figure 1 - Stages in a HACCP Study in Agriculture

Stage 1	Define the terms of reference
Stage 2	Select the HACCP team
Stage 3	Describe the essential product characteristics
Stage 4	Construct a flow diagram
Stage 5	List all potential hazards associated with each process step, conduct a hazard analysis and consider any measures to control identified hazards *(Principle 1)*
Stage 6	Determine Critical Control Points (CCPs) *(Principle 2)*
Stage 7	Establish critical limits for each CCP *(Principle 3)*
Stage 8	Establish a monitoring system for each CCP *(Principle 4)*
Stage 9	Establish a corrective action plan *(Principle 5)*
Stage 10	Establish verification procedures *(Principle 6)*
Stage 11	Establish documentation and record keeping *(Principle 7)*
Stage 12	Review the HACCP plan

Before the beef HACCP study begins, it is essential that there is full commitment at all levels of management in order that the necessary resources, including relevant personnel, are provided to develop and implement the HACCP system.

1.1   Planning Stages

Stage 1: Define the terms of reference

A beef HACCP study should be taken on a specific rearing enterprise and/or a specific range of activities. In order for the study to be quickly developed, easily implemented and fully effective it is essential that the scope of the study is outlined clearly at the outset. It is therefore necessary to define factors such as:

- Study objective - for example, a statement as to whether meat safety and/or quality aspects are to be considered and at what point in the production operation these are to be considered.
- Animal and rearing details - for example, a statement of the type of animal, location of the animal production operation and production activities to be included in the study.
- Hazards - for example, a statement defining which biological, chemical and physical safety and/or quality hazards are to be considered.

Stage 2: Select the HACCP team

Depending on the size and nature of the operation, development and implementation of the system should, wherever possible, be undertaken by a team who have adequate knowledge and expertise in order to undertake the study, including knowledge of cattle and the rearing process and an understanding of HACCP principles and their application.

It is desirable for a small group of individuals to undertake the study. These individuals should have appropriate training and experience, but may also seek specialist advice from outside the group as necessary. It is feasible for one person to develop the system but this individual should have full understanding of the operation, and should wherever necessary seek specialist support or information, to ensure that the study is effective.

The individuals involved in the study should be identified; preferably this should include a statement of their relevant knowledge and expertise.

Stage 3: Describe the essential product characteristics

A full description of the animal rearing enterprise under study should be prepared, including definitions of key parameters which influence the safety and/or quality of the product (these will be used in Stage 6). The essential product characteristics to be considered in a beef study include:

- Animal product description (beef, Aberdeen Angus beef)
- Rearing conditions
- Handling and transport conditions
- Intended use of the product

The intended use should identify the market and/or the customer requirements - and should encompass any special considerations relevant to the product.

Stage 4: Construct a flow diagram

Prior to starting the hazard analysis it is necessary to define the animal production process. This will involve careful examination of the stages in the cattle rearing system and inputs (e.g. feed) and the production of a flow diagram around which the study can be based.

There are no rules for the format of the flow diagram (presentation is a matter of preference), except that all of the key steps in the process (for example, from animal rearing, slaughter and transport to customer) should be clearly outlined in a logical sequence. The flow diagram should provide sufficient technical detail for the study to proceed. The amount of detail shown in the flow diagram in respect of the identification of the steps in the process will depend on the objectives of the study and nature of the business.

Examples of the type of detail that may be included in a beef production flow diagram are:

- Rearing environment practices
- Inputs - feed, water and veterinary treatments
- Transport

1.2 Application Stages

Stage 5: Hazards and controls (Principle 1)

Using the flow diagram (Stage 4) as a guide, all the potential hazards, as defined in the scope of the study (Stage 1) that may reasonably be expected to occur at each step should be identified. The consideration should include hazards that may be present in the animals and hazards that may be introduced during the animal rearing process (for example, contamination from the environment, personnel and equipment). In animal production operations, contamination may be the main risk but presence and survival should not be ignored as potential risks. There should be a deliberate policy to ensure that all realistic hazards are identified.

It may be helpful to identify the cause of the hazard, as this may help determine the control measures. The appendix table gives examples of hazards and controls.

The next step is to specify the control measures that are applied for each identified hazard. Control measures are actions or activities that are applied to eliminate or reduce the hazard to an acceptable level. In practice this may mean defining usual practices in terms of animal rearing.

Examples of controls include: documented policies, staff training, approved veterinary treatments and conditions of approval (product label recommendations). Where appropriate, control measures need to be underpinned by detailed criteria and/or policies and procedures (see Stage 11) to ensure their effective implementation.

Stage 6: Determine Critical Control Points (Principle 2)

For each hazard identified in Stage 5, determine whether the process step is a Critical Control Point (CCP). The identification of CCPs requires professional judgement and may be aided by the use of a decision tree.

There is no limit to the number of CCPs that may be identified in an animal production study. In practice, there will be many CCPs in a beef production process because there are few, if any, specific steps in the process (as defined in Stage 4) that will eliminate or reduce meat safety and quality hazards to an acceptable limit.

Stage 7: Establish critical limits for each CCP (Principle 3)

For each CCP, the critical limits for the control measures should be identified. The critical limit is the predetermined value for the control measure applied at each CCP, and is the criterion which separates acceptability from unacceptability. It should represent some measurable related parameter that can be assessed quickly and easily in Stage 8.

In animal rearing, critical limits are generally of two types:

- Quantifiable values, such as approved veterinary treatments
- Compliance with a policy or procedure, such as staff training.

Stage 8: Establish a monitoring system for each CCP (Principle 4)

Monitoring is a planned sequence of observations or measurements of CCP control measures. The monitoring system describes the methods which confirm that all CCPs are in control. It also produces a record of performance for future use in verification (Stage 10). Monitoring must also be able to detect loss of control at the CCP so that corrective action can be taken to regain control (Stage 9).

The monitoring system should preferably address three issues:

- *how* the monitoring is to be carried out - that is, what measurement or observation is being carried out
- *when* the monitoring is to be carried out - that is, at what frequency the measurement or observation is carried out
- *who* has responsibility for carrying out the monitoring

Stage 9: Establish a corrective action plan (Principle 5)

If, in the process of monitoring (Stage 8), it is found that there is a loss of control, it is important that appropriate action is taken. Corrective actions should aim to bring the animal production process back under control and deal with the affected animals where appropriate. Corrective actions should preferably involve the consideration of:

- *what* went wrong
- *what* is going to be done with the product if it is judged to be non-conforming - that is, out of specification in terms of safety and/or quality criteria
- *how* it can be stopped from happening again
- *who* has responsibility for the actions taken.

It is important that the action taken is logical and rational and should involve a thorough review.

Stage 10: Establish verification procedures (Principle 6)

Verification procedures are used to demonstrate compliance with the HACCP plan - that is, that it is operating correctly and effectively. Verification should, therefore, examine the entire HACCP system including records.

Examples of verification in animal production include:

- Audits of records and associated procedures. These may be internal by the business and/or external by independent third parties such as customers and verifiers of assurance schemes.
- Monitoring customer satisfaction, e.g. reports from the abattoir
- End product testing - for example, veterinary residue analysis to verify compliance with Maximum Residue Limits (MRLs).
- Review of the HACCP plan (see Stage 12)

Stage 11: Establish documentation and record keeping (Principle 7)

It is important for the beef producer to be able to demonstrate that the principles of HACCP have been applied correctly, and that documentation and records have been kept in a way appropriate to the nature and size of the business. Records provide evidence that systems operate as specified.

Examples of animal production documentation include:

- Documentation of the system (the HACCP plan)
- Operating procedures and management policies
- Codes of Practice

Examples of animal production records include:

- Operational records, including animal monitoring data, veterinary treatments application data, training records (relating to Stage 5)
- Monitoring data (relating to Stage 8)
- Corrective actions taken (relating to Stage 9)
- Verification data (relating to Stage 10)

The retention period for records should also be considered and defined.

Stage 12: Review the HACCP plan

A periodic review of the HACCP plan should be carried out. For beef production this may be once a year at an appropriate time during the rearing cycle. It is essential that the review should consider any changes which affect the HACCP plan or animal production system prior to their implementation. In addition, there should be an automatic assessment to determine if a review is required when a change occurs outside the normal review period.

Examples of changes that may trigger an automatic review are:

- Change in the animal production process
- New equipment
- Change in staff levels and/or responsibilities
- Anticipated change in customer use/requirements
- Change in legislation

The review of the HACCP plan may form part of verification (Stage 10).

SECTION 2: Worked example of a beef HACCP study

To demonstrate the application of HACCP principles in beef production, a single worked example is presented. The level of detail of the HACCP system will depend on the nature and size of the animal production operation.

In this example the approach has been to include all aspects of rearing the animal as one step, from birth through to maturity. It is possible to produce a more detailed study and to examine each stage in the rearing process separately. This may be appropriate in larger enterprises, so that separate locations (buildings or pasture) and husbandry practices can be considered separately

It must be stressed that:

- the details given are not exhaustive
- the examples should not be taken as specific recommendations for similar animal production operations
- the information is not intended for direct use, but only as a demonstration of how the principles of HACCP can be applied to beef production
- the details given are for guidance only and will depend on specific circumstances.

The examples have been developed using the 12 stages in a HACCP study in agriculture (see Figure 1). However, some details, such as procedural references for control measures, are not shown. Other details, such as monitoring procedures, corrective actions, verification and documentation are shown for indication only and will always depend on specific circumstances.

EXAMPLE: BEEF PRODUCTION

Terms of reference (Stage 1)

- Scope of the study
  This is a demonstration study covering food safety hazards and key product quality aspects at the point of transport for slaughter.

- Animal and production details
  The study covers animal rearing for beef at (*location of the beef production operation specified*), from arrival/birth of the animal on the farm to transport to the abattoir.

- Hazards

  Three categories of hazard are considered: biological, chemical and physical; for example:

BIOLOGICAL	CHEMICAL	PHYSICAL
• Pathogenic bacteria (*E.coli*, *Salmonella*, etc.)	• Veterinary residues (including pesticides, antibiotics or other pharmacological products)	• Fat*
• BSE		• Conformation*
		• Breed*
	• Heavy metals	• Taint*
	• Pesticide residues from crops	

  * Quality characteristics

Two hazards have been selected for illustration here: pathogenic bacteria (biological) and veterinary residues (chemical). The same methods of working would be employed to construct a HACCP for other safety and quality hazards.

HACCP team and skills (Stage 2)

Farm manager (husbandry and management skills)
Farm foreman (animal production and veterinary application skills)
Quality manager (quality control and HACCP skills)

Essential product characteristics (Stage 3)

- Animal product:
  Beef of specified breed/cross, ready for slaughter at 16 months.

- Rearing conditions:
  Cattle bred and reared on farm or bought in (see Figure 2). Animals on pasture in summer and housed in winter.

- Intended use:
  Beef for retail sale in the UK.

Flow diagram (Stage 4)

The steps in the beef production process are shown in Figure 2. A description of each step is given in Table 1.

Hazard analysis (Stages 5 to 9)

The hazard analysis is summarised in Table 1. The potential hazards at each step in the process have been identified and the measures for their control specified. CCPs have been determined using a decision tree. This process is described in detail in *HACCP in Agriculture: Livestock Production (CCFRA Guideline 33)*. It should be noted that all the steps with an identified hazard are CCPs. This is because there are no steps in this beef production process that will eliminate or reduce the hazards to acceptable levels.

For each CCP, the critical limits, monitoring procedures and corrective actions have been established (see Table 1). These are shown for indication only and will depend on specific circumstances.

Verification (Stages 10 and 12)

The following verification procedures are undertaken:

- Audits of the HACCP system, including:
  Internal audits: Self assessments including business specific audits which are scheduled on the basis of history and risk.

  External audits: Inspections by customers and verification audits for assurance schemes such as Farm Assured British Beef and Lamb (FABBL).

- Monitoring and analysis of customer satisfaction, including abattoir reports.
- Finished product testing - for example, veterinary residue analysis.
- Review of the HACCP system:

Periodic reviews: once per year

Review prior to significant changes (outside the periodic review).

Documentation and record keeping (Stage 11)

The following documents are retained:

- The HACCP plan
- Management policies and operational procedures
- Codes of practice, Assurance Scheme Standards eg FABBL, specifications.

The following records are retained:

- Operational records - for example, feed company documentation, movement books, veterinary treatments and training records
- Monitoring data
- Corrective actions taken
- Verification data

Figure 2

Flow diagram outlining cattle rearing for beef production

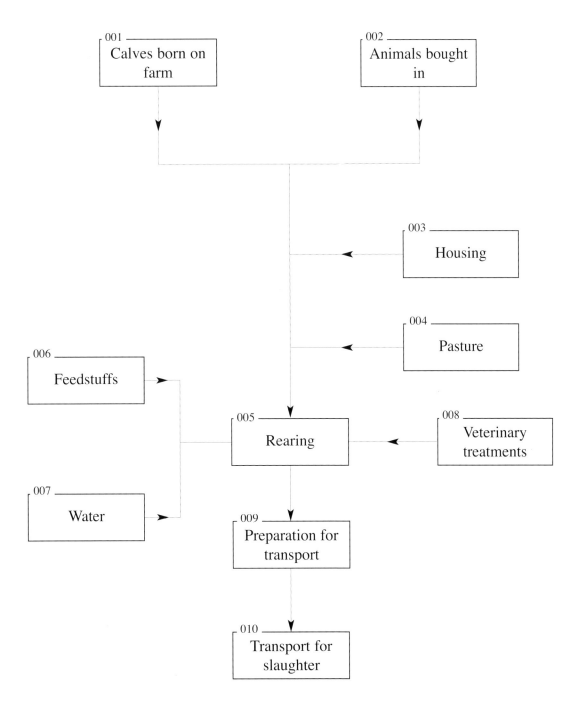

Table 1

Study Beef Production	HACCP Analysis	
Prepared by	Issue Number	Date of Issue

Process step	Hazards	Control	CCP Question 1	2	3	4	CCP	Critical limit	Monitoring procedure	Corrective action
001 Calves born on farm - from conception to birth	1. None identified									
002 Animals brought in - animals (calves or older stock) brought in from other holdings for rearing	1. Presence of pathogens in brought-in stock	1.1 Use reliable suppliers	Yes	No	Yes	No	Yes	Purchase from clean herd	Check health record of herd of origin and policy on preventative actions (e.g. vaccination)	Review suppliers
		1.2 Keep new animals in quarantine and/or keep on farm for minimum period before slaughter.						Period of observation (quarantine/minimum period before slaughter)	Scheduled visual checks of quarantined stock by appropriately trained/experienced staff	Review status of animal Review period of observation.
003 Housing - buildings and bedding	1. Infection with pathogens through injury in unsafe buildings	1.1 Safety policy. Follow advice in 'Code of recommendations for the welfare of livestock - cattle'	Yes	No	Yes	No	Yes	Compliance with 'Code of recommendations for the welfare of livestock - cattle'	Record scheduled visual safety checks of buildings, by appropriately trained/experienced staff	Treat animals for injury or infection. Rectify and repair buildings. Review staff training.
004 Pasture - land to be grazed	1. Contamination or infection of animals with pathogens from FYM or slurry e.g. *E. coli*	1.1 Follow GAP - grazing interval, stack manure and store slurry as recommended.	Yes	No	Yes	No	Yes	Compliance with acceptable GAP	Scheduled check of records - dates of spreading and grazing	Review status of affected animals. Review GAP re spreading and grazing
	2. Contamination or infection of animals from sewage sludge	2.1 GAP - follow Code of Practice for Agricultural Use of Sewage Sludge and the 'Safe Sludge Matrix'	Yes	No	Yes	No	Yes	Compliance with 'Code of Practice for Agricultural Use of Sewage Sludge' including the 'Safe Sludge Matrix' and observation of 3 week grazing interval.	Scheduled check of records - dates of spreading and grazing.	Review status of affected animals. Review GAP re-use of sewage sludge and grazing. Review suppliers.
005 Rearing - animal husbandry during life of animal	1. Contamination or infection of animals with pathogens from other herd members	1.1 Veterinary treatment and Preventative treatment policy.	Yes	No	Yes	No	Yes	Suitable product and dose rate administered by trained staff.	Check veterinary records.	Review health status of animal. Review veterinary treatment and preventative measures.

Study	Beef Production	HACCP Analysis
Prepared by	Issue Number	Date of Issue

Process step	Hazards	Control	CCP Question 1	2	3	4	CCP	Critical limit	Monitoring procedure	Corrective action
		1.2 Segregate clinically ill animals until recovered.						Clinically ill animals clearly identified and segregated, if necessary through to slaughter.	Check veterinary records and location of affected animals. Scheduled visual check by appropriately trained/experienced staff.	Review facilities and procedures for sick animals.
		1.3 GHP - Appropriate stocking densities. Follow guidelines in 'Code of recommendations for the welfare of livestock - cattle'						Compliance with 'Code of recommendations for the welfare of livestock - cattle'	Scheduled check of records - numbers of cattle against capacity of buildings. Scheduled visual check of stock, by appropriately trained/experienced staff.	Veterinary treatment for infected animals. Review GHP.
	2. Infection with pathogens from wounds	2.1 Veterinary treatment of injured animals and monitoring of their recovery.	Yes	No	Yes	No	Yes	Wounds treated as necessary with suitable product and dose rate.	Check veterinary records.	Review veterinary treatment.
		2.2 GHP - prevention of wounds						Acceptable GHP	Scheduled visual checks by appropriately trained/experienced staff.	Review staff training. Review GHP - safety policy.
	3. Contamination or infection of animals with pathogens from vermin (rodents, birds and other pests) or from farm dogs or from other species of farm animal.	3.1 Premises designed and maintained to exclude pests	Yes	No	Yes	No	Yes	Buildings pest proof	Scheduled visual inspections of buildings and visual inspection for presence of pests.	Review status of affected animals. Review procedures and take appropriate action to remedy defects in premises. Control pests.
		3.2 Pest control measures carried out.						Pest control procedures adhered to.	Scheduled check of records. Visual inspection for pests. Check training of contractors.	Review procedures and take appropriate action to remedy pest activity.

Study Beef Production   HACCP Analysis

Prepared by	Issue Number	Date of Issue

Process step	Hazards	Control	CCP Question 1	2	3	4	CCP	Critical limit	Monitoring procedure	Corrective action
		3.3 House different species of farm animals separately.						Different species housed separately.	Scheduled checks of buildings for signs of presence of other species and for defects in barriers to their entry.	Review housing re security from other species of farm stock.
	5. Contamination or infection with pathogens from humans.	4.1 GHP - Follow advice in 'Code of recommendations for the welfare of livestock - cattle' and 'Clean beef for slaughter'. Change/top up with bedding of suitable quality, as appropriate and maintain cleanliness of buildings.	Yes	No	Yes	No	Yes	Compliance with 'Code of recommendations for the welfare of livestock - cattle' and 'Clean beef for slaughter'.	Scheduled visual check of stock, of cleanliness of buildings and bedding by appropriately trained/experienced staff.	Review status of affected animals and decide if veterinary treatment is appropriate. Review GHP. Review staff training.
		5.1 Hygiene policy including Personal Protective Clothing.	Yes	No	Yes	No	Yes	Hygiene policy adhered to by staff.	Scheduled visual check of provision and wearing of protective clothing, hygienic practices etc.	Review status of affected animals and decide if veterinary treatment is appropriate. Review hygiene policy.
		5.2 Access policy for staff and visitors.						Access policy for staff and visitors adhered to.	Visual check of procedures.	Review access policy.
		5.3 Staff training						Trained personnel.	Check training records.	Review staff training.
006 Feedstuffs - bought or home produced feeds.	1. Infection of animals with pathogens from components in feeds including those mixed on the farm.	1.1 Approved suppliers following 'Feedingstuff Regulations'. 'Good Practice - UKASTA code of practice for manufacture of safe animal feed.	Yes	No	Yes	No	Yes	Approved suppliers supplying feeds of suitable quality.	Scheduled checks of visual quality of feed at delivery (i.e. no visible mould). Check warranties from suppliers.	Report problem to suppliers. Review procedures.

Study Beef Production HACCP Analysis		
Prepared by	Issue Number	Date of Issue

Process step	Hazards	Control	CCP Question 1	CCP Question 2	CCP Question 3	CCP Question 4	CCP	Critical limit	Monitoring procedure	Corrective action
		1.2 Home mixers follow good practice - 'UKASTA code of practice for manufacture of safe animal feed' and practice rotation of stocks of feedstuffs.						Adhere to good practice, including rotation of stocks of feedstuffs.	Scheduled checks of visual quality of feed (i.e. no visible mould).	Review procedures.
	2. Infection with pathogens from farm stored food-stuffs caused by vermin (e.g. birds, rodents).	2.1 Pest control regime	Yes	No	Yes	No	Yes	Adhere to pest control regime	Scheduled check of pest control records. Scheduled inspection of storage facilities for defects and pest activity.	Review status of feedstuffs and dispose of them if necessary. Review pest control regime.
	3. Infection of animals with pathogens from farm stored foodstuffs caused by the environment.	3.1 Follow 'Code of practice for the control of *Salmonella* during storage, handling and transport of raw materials etc' for building design.	Yes	No	Yes	No	Yes	Adhere to code of practice.	Visual check of buildings for weatherproof condition.	Review building design and correct faults.
		3.2 Hygiene Policy - See 'Code of practice for the control of *Salmonella* during storage, handling and transport of raw materials etc'.						Adhere to hygiene policy for storage.	Scheduled visual inspection of hygiene measures in stores.	Review status of feeds and dispose of them if necessary. Review hygiene policy.
	4. Infection of animals with pathogens from components in forage.	4.1 Follow GAP in making and storing forage (e.g. hay and silage).	Yes	No	Yes	No	Yes	Adhere to GAP for production and storage of forages.	Scheduled visual checks of quality during making and storage of forage by appropriate trained/ experienced staff.	Review status of feeds and dispose of them if necessary. Review GAP. Review staff training.
	5. Residues in the meat of antibiotics, pesticides or other pharmacological substances from compound feeds.	5.1 Approved suppliers providing Medicated Feedingstuff (MFS). Directives for medicated feeds.	Yes	No	Yes	No	Yes	Approved suppliers used and MFS supplied and signed by vet for all medicated feeds.	Check MFS supplied.	Report problem to feed manufacturer. Review suppliers.

Study: Beef Production HACCP Analysis

Prepared by | Issue Number | Date of Issue

Process step	Hazards	Control	CCP Question					Critical limit	Monitoring procedure	Corrective action
			1	2	3	4	CCP			
		5.2 Follow manufacturers' instructions on feeding rates.						Recommended feeding rates not exceeded.	Scheduled check of feedstuff records, including purchases in line with usage. Scheduled maintenance of equipment for measuring feeds. Scheduled calibration and maintenance of measuring equipment.	Review procedures.
		5.3 Separate different feeds, particularly medicated from unmedicated.						Different types of feed for different livestock enterprises stored separately - e.g. in separate bins.	Scheduled visual check of stored feeds. Checks on filling of bins at delivery to avoid mixing different lots.	Review storage facilities and procedures.
		5.4 Train staff in correct procedures						Feedstuffs prepared by appropriately trained staff.	Scheduled check of staff procedures followed.	Review staff training.
		5.5 Identify group of animals requiring medicated feed and ensure it is not fed to any other animals.						Medicated feed only fed to correctly identified animals.	Scheduled visual check of feed bins and contents. Scheduled visual check of housing of animals. Scheduled checks of feed records.	Review status of animals. Review procedures.
		5.6 Home mixers obtain Medicated Feedingstuffs (MFS) Directives for medicated feeds						MFS directives obtained and signed by vet and information adhered to.	Scheduled check of medicated feedstuff information - e.g. bag labels and Medicated Feedingstuffs (MFS) directives.	Review status of animals. Review precedure.
007 Water supply	1. Infection or contamination of animals with pathogens from water.	1.1 Use of suitable water supply. Follow guidelines in 'Code of recommendations for the welfare of livestock - cattle'.						Clean, fresh water.	Scheduled visual checks of water. Scheduled testing of non-mains supplies.	Review status of animal. Give veterinary treatment if appropriate. Review sources and quality of water. Review hygiene policy and procedures.

	Study	Beef Production	HACCP Analysis
	Prepared by	Issue Number	Date of Issue

Process step	Hazards	Control	CCP Question					Critical limit	Monitoring procedure	Corrective action
			1	2	3	4	CCP			
		1.2 Container hygiene						Clean containers used.	Scheduled visual checks of container cleanliness.	Review container hygiene procedures.
008 Veterinary treatments - treatment for disease or accident.	1. Residues of antibiotics and other veterinary medicines due to incorrect use.	1.1 Approved products and correct dose rates.	Yes	No	Yes	No	Yes	Use approved products and correct dose rates.	Scheduled check of veterinary records.	Review procedures.
		1.2 Withdrawal period.						Adhere to withdrawal period.	Scheduled check of veterinary records.	Review procedures.
		1.3 Staff training in use and administering of veterinary products.						Use trained staff.	Scheduled check of training records.	Review training procedures.
	2. Residues of veterinary medicines in 'casualty animals' entering the human food chain.	2.1 Comply with legislation for casualty animals						Legislation complied with.	Scheduled check of movement records.	Review procedures and staff training.
	3. Residues of veterinary medicines in animals slaughtered on farm entering the human food chain.	3.1 Comply with legislation for animals slaughtered on farm						Legislation complied with.	Scheduled check of movement records.	Review procedures and staff training.
009 Preparation for transport - management changes during few weeks before transport.	1. None identified.									

	Study	Beef Production	HACCP Analysis	
	Prepared by	Issue Number	Date of Issue	

Process step	Hazards	Control	CCP Question				CCP	Critical limit	Monitoring procedure	Corrective action
			1	2	3	4				
010 Transport for slaughter - transport conditions and loading.	1. Presence of pathogens on coats of dirty animals leading to rejection at abattoir.	1.1 Preparation procedure - follow 'Clean Livestock Policy'.	Yes	No	Yes	Yes	No	CLP Categories 1 and 2.	Visual examination of animals before loading by appropriately trained/experienced staff.	Review preparation procedures and staff training.
	2. Presence of pathogens on outside of unclean animals and contamination of clean animals.	2.1 Follow Clean Livestock Policy.	Yes	No	Yes	No	Yes	CLP Categories 1 and 2.	Visual examination of animals before loading by appropriately trained/experienced staff.	Review procedures
		2.2 Segregation of stock from different holdings.						Segregation in the lorry.	Check transport before loading.	Review transporter. Review segregation procedures.
	3. Infection with pathogens of animals injured in transport.	3.1 Follow transport policy.	Yes	No	Yes	No	Yes	Safe transport conditions.	Examine tranport for safety (no sharp edges).	Review procedures. Review tranporters.
	4. Increased growth of pathogens in or on animals during transport, due to stress.	4.1 Follow clean livestock policy - avoid overcrowding.	Yes	No	Yes	No	Yes	Adhere to clean livestock policy - relate numbers of animals to size of lorry.	Scheduled visual check at loading.	Review procedures.
		4.2 Use trained staff (to avoid stressing animals at loading).						Trained staff loading animals correctly.	Scheduled visual check of loading procedures. Scheduled check of training records.	Review staff training.
	5. Contamination of animals with pathogens from the vehicle.	5.1 Examine transport for cleanliness before loading own stock.	Yes	No	Yes	No	Yes	Transport in clean condition before animals are loaded.	Scheduled visual check at loading.	Review transport companies used.

Study	Beef Production	HACCP Analysis
Prepared by	Issue Number	Date of Issue

Process step	Hazards	Control	CCP Question					Critical limit	Monitoring procedure	Corrective action
			1	2	3	4	CCP			
	6. Pathogens from 'casualty animals' entering the human food chain.	6.1 Comply with legislation for casualty animals	Yes	No	Yes	No	Yes	Legislation complied with.	Scheduled check of movement records.	Review procedures and staff training.
	7. Pathogens from animals slaughtered on farm entering the human food chain.	7.1 Comply with legislation for animals slaughtered on farm	Yes	No	Yes	No	Yes	Legislation complied with.	Scheduled check of movement records.	Review procedures and staff training.

Abbreviations

GAP	- Good Agricultural Practice
GHP	- Good Husbandry Practice
UKASTA	- United Kingdom Agricultural Supply Trade Association
MFS	- Medicated Feedingstuffs Directive
(s)	- safety
(q)	- quality

APPENDIX: Example Hazards and Controls

Some typical control measures for three examples of hazards in a beef rearing enterprise; two for safety and one for quality

Examples of some common hazards and causes and typical control measures

Hazard	Cause or source of contamination	Control
Pathogenic bacteria	From stock brought on to the holding	• Use reliable suppliers • New animals quarantined or retained for a minimum period on the farm before slaughter
	Passed from other herd members during rearing	• Adherence to Good Animal Husbandry Practices (GHP) including suitable stocking densities • Veterinary treatment for animals with visible symptoms • Preventative treatment such as vaccination if appropriate
	At transport to abattoir - from other animals, stress, from the transport	• Adherence to 'Clean livestock policy' including pre transport cleaning phase if necessary
Veterinary residues	From veterinary products	• Use of approved products, at correct dose rates • Adherence to correct withdrawal period • Staff trained in correct administration procedures for veterinary medicines • Identificaiton of animals receiving veterinary treatment

Examples of some common hazards and causes and typical control measures (continued)

Hazard	Cause or source of contamination	Control
Veterinary residues (continued)	From feed	• Use of approved feed suppliers providing Medicated Feedingstuff (MFS) Directives for medicated feeds • Adherence to legislation for home mixed feeds • Adherence to correct feeding rates • Correct storage separating medicated from unmedicated feed • Identification of animals receiving medicated feed • Staff trained in correct administration procedures for medicated feeds
Carcass quality e.g. unsuitable for end use - poor grade out at the abattoir	Use of unsuitable breed	• Selection of suitable stock for rearing
	Poor animal husbandry	• Trained staff following Good Husbandry Practices (GHP) for care of animals to give healthy growth • Correct feeding regimes • Selecting animals for slaughter at correct age, weight and conformation